At the Match

Written by Roderick Hunt and Annemarie Young
Illustrated by Alex Brychta

Sam was excited. Rush Green was through to Round 3 of the FA Cup. It was only a small team, but now it would play against East Ham.

Sam's dad was the captain of Rush Green.

"The match will be on TV," said Sam.

“When we play East Ham,” Sam said, “I’ll lead the team onto the pitch. I’m the mascot for this game.”

“Brilliant!” said Kipper.

When Kipper got home, he was excited. Sam's mum had invited Kipper to go to the big match with them.

“It’s not fair,” said Chip. “Kipper doesn’t even like football.”

“Stop it, Chip,” said Dad. “Maybe I can take you and Biff to the match.”

The next day Dad tried to buy tickets for the match, but they were sold out. Chip and Biff were disappointed.

When Sam came round to show off his football strip, Chip went up to his room and slammed the door.

Kipper went to the match with Sam's mum and grandad. A big crowd of people was moving towards the gate.

Kipper went through a turnstile into the football ground.

"If you need the toilet, you'd better go now," said Sam's mum.

They had special seats next to the tunnel.

"The players come out onto the pitch here," said Grandad.

There were thousands of fans in the stands. All the Rush Green fans were at one end. They all wore green and white.

Hammy, the East Ham club mascot, came onto the pitch. There was a huge roar from the East Ham fans. “It’s so loud,” said Kipper.

There was a great cheer from all the fans as the players ran on. Sam was next to his dad. He carried the ball.

The Rush Green team lined up for a photo. Then it was time for the match to begin.

Sam came and sat next to Kipper.
"Come on Rush Green!" yelled Sam.
Rush Green had the ball in the
East Ham half of the pitch.

A Rush Green player kicked a high cross into the penalty area. Sam's dad headed the ball . . . and scored! The Rush Green fans went wild!

At half-time, Sam's mum went to get hot pies.

"Wow!" said Sam. "Rush Green is leading by one goal in the first half."

“One up!” said Kipper. “Ace!”

Their excitement didn’t last. East Ham were in the Rush Green end for most of the second half.

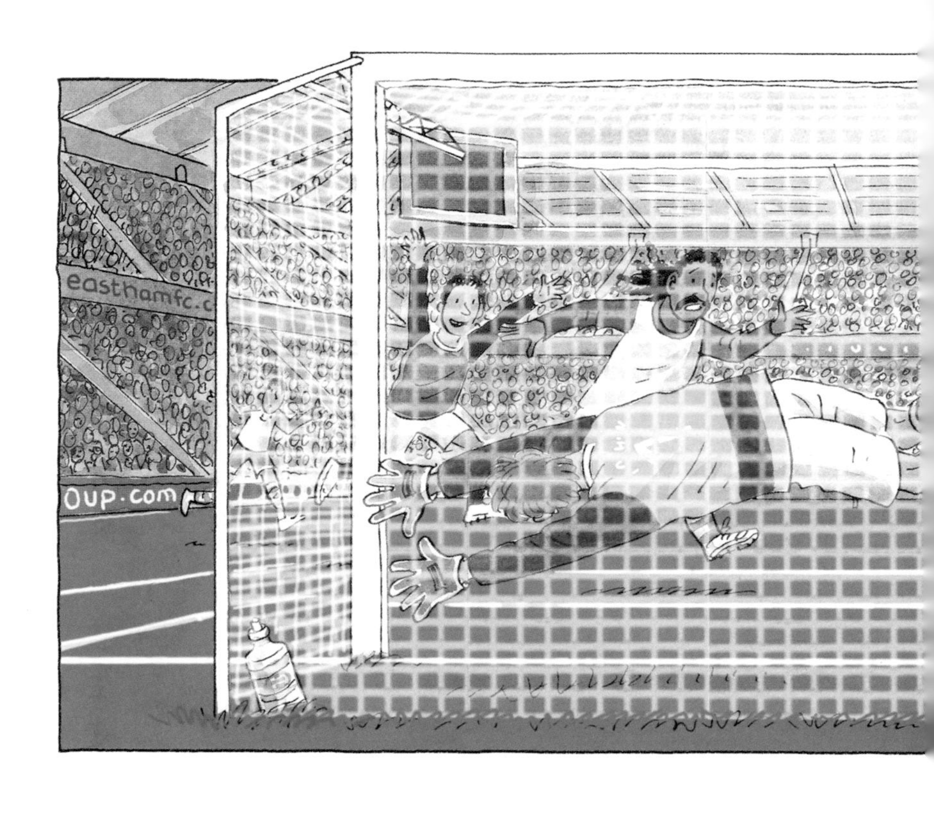

The East Ham players began to look strong. The ball slammed into the crossbar – almost a goal! Ten minutes later, they scored.

Then a Rush Green player fouled an East Ham striker – a penalty to East Ham! They took it and scored.

"Oh no! Two–one," said Sam.

“Two–one. Sorry, Dad,” said Sam after the match was over.

“It was good to score,” said Sam’s dad. “We didn’t expect to win.”

Sam's dad had a present for Sam and Kipper – footballs signed by all the East Ham players.

"Fantastic," said Kipper.

“This is for you,” said Kipper.

“And this is for you,” said Chip. “We recorded the match. It was great seeing you on TV.”

Talk about the story

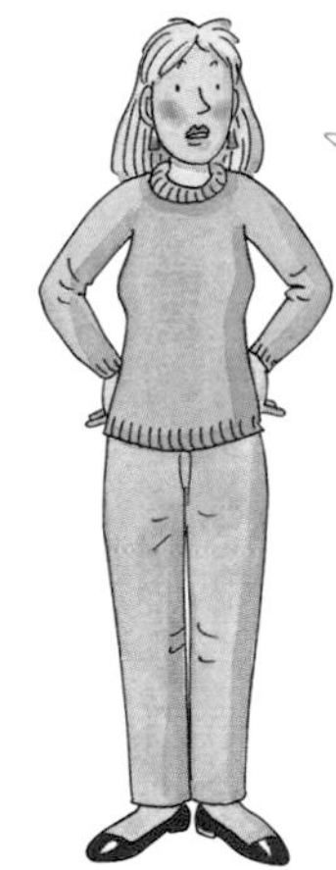

Why was
Sam excited?

Why did Chip
slam the door?

How did
the match end?

What makes
watching a football
match so exciting?

The football pitch

Halfway line
Corner flag
Penalty box
Centre circle
Penalty spot
Centre spot
Goal
6 yard box
Goal-line
Touchline

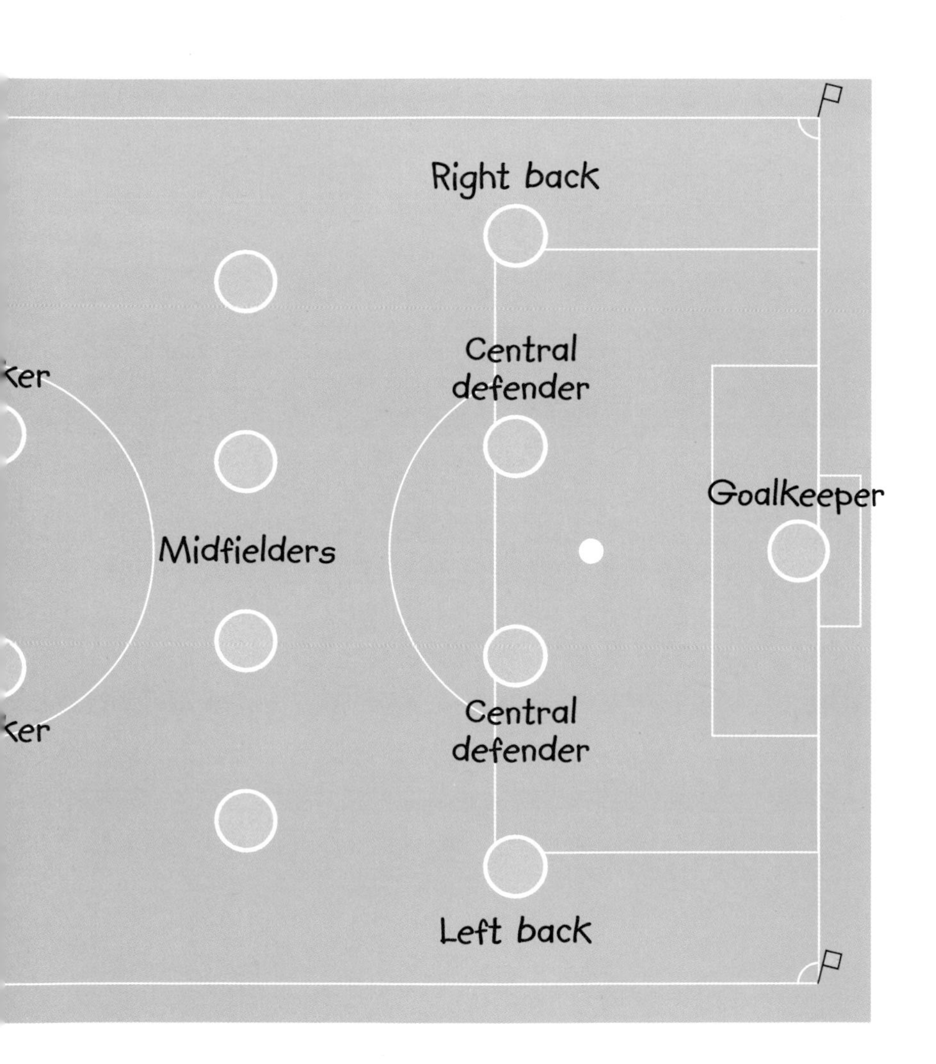
Right back
Central defender
Goalkeeper
Midfielders
Central defender
Left back

Spot the difference

Find the 5 differences in the two pictures of Sam.